SONGS FOR THE YOUNG CHURCH CHOIR

*A first collection of 25 attractive pieces
compiled by Kevin Mayhew*

Kevin
Mayhew

We hope you enjoy *Songs for the Young Church Choir*.
Further copies are available from your local
music shop or Christian bookshop.

In case of difficulty, please contact the publisher direct by writing to:

The Sales Department
KEVIN MAYHEW LTD
Rattlesden
Bury St Edmunds
Suffolk
IP30 0SZ

Phone 01449 737978
Fax 01449 737834

Please ask for our complete catalogue of outstanding Church Music.

First published in Great Britain in 1996 by Kevin Mayhew Ltd

© Copyright 1996 Kevin Mayhew Ltd

ISBN 0 86209 815 7
Catalogue No: 1450048

Front Cover: *Missal 515 f.144v Angels Singing* (1448-1449)
by Zanobi di Benedetto Strozzi (1412-1468)
Courtesy of Museo di San Marco dell'Angelico, Florence/
The Bridgeman Art Library, London. Reproduced by kind permission.

Cover design by Graham Johnstone and Veronica Ward

Music Editors: Rosalind Dean and Donald Thomson
Music setting by Stephanie Hill

Printed and bound in Great Britain

Contents

Foreword

The story behind this collection of songs for young people's choirs is simply told.

Having trained and conducted a number of adult choirs over the years, I unexpectedly found myself responsible for forming and directing a junior choir in my parish church. My only previous experience in this area was when, as a boy soprano, I was a member of the Choir of Westminster Cathedral, London, when George Malcolm was the innovative and inspirational Master of Music.

In my inexperience I clearly needed to work out some basic principles for both the choir and myself if we were to meet the parish requirement that we lead the worship on at least one Sunday a month, just as the adult choir and the music group did.

It was necessary, first of all, to establish that the children were to be treated as proper church choral singers, and that the rules applying to good adult choirs also applied to them: regular attendance at the weekly rehearsal and services; proper reverence during services; and musical standards that could stand critical appraisal. Our Young People's Choir was to be appreciated not just because 'it is lovely to hear the children sing' (which we hope it is), but because it was capable of leading the parish in exactly the same manner as its adult equivalent.

Although the circumstances and demands are different, this is obviously the basis upon which cathedral choirs are run, and my memory of my own cathedral days was that we sang beautifully because George Malcolm expected us to and would have been rather surprised if we had not.

The result in our parish has been a choir which sounds well and is enormously enthusiastic (we have 35 members from 7 to 12 years and as near to 100 per cent attendance as it is possible to get). Besides our musical activities in our own and other churches, we also enjoy a regular social life which adds cohesion to the choir.

One difficulty I had not foreseen was the lack of suitable music for the newly-formed choir. There was, on the one hand, plenty of what American publishers call 'cutesie' material which was not the kind of thing I was looking for, and, on the other hand, fine music which we could not use, either because it went too high or too low, or made demands which the children's voices could not cope with at the beginning of their singing careers.

I wanted words and music in a variety of styles that had substance and did not speak down to the children; material that would present them with a God who loves each one of us, wants us to love each other and who cares for his creation: music the children would enjoy learning and singing. If, as a publisher with easy access to what is available, I had problems in finding material, what of everyone else?

The music in this book represents not only my choice, but also, through their enthusiasm for a piece, the choice of the children. There is no particular theme or pattern to it: we just hope that it will be as useful and enjoyable to others as it has been for us.

Although a few of these songs are for the choir to sing alone, the greater number can include an element of congregational involvement when desired by way of their refrain. Four (*Come and bring your gifts;*

Praise our God; Praise to the Lord; The Lord comes down from heaven) are written as a dialogue between soloist or cantor, congregation and choir, and sound very effective when performed in this way.

The collection represents much of what we sung as a choir during services in our first year. At the end of the year we gave a concert which included many of these songs.

In our second year we are doing more pieces in parts and have already performed to a full and appreciative church the mini-musical *Singing, Dancing Carpenter* by Michael Forster and Christopher Tambling (Kevin Mayhew). A glance through the contents of this book will show how much we rely on the work of these two talented writers. I am grateful to them and to the other composers for their contributions.

I hope this first volume of *Songs for the Young Church Choir* will be found enjoyable and useful. When we have completed our second year we will share our songs again.

KEVIN MAYHEW

*For the Saint Edmund's Young People's Choir,
Bury St Edmunds, Suffolk, England*

COME AND BRING YOUR GIFTS

Text: Hubert J. Richards
Music: Richard Shephard

Solo

Come and bring your gifts to the Lord.

Choir and Congregation

Come and bring your gifts to the Lord.

Solo

Our help is in the name of the Lord.

Choir and Congregation

Our help is in the name of the Lord.

Ped.

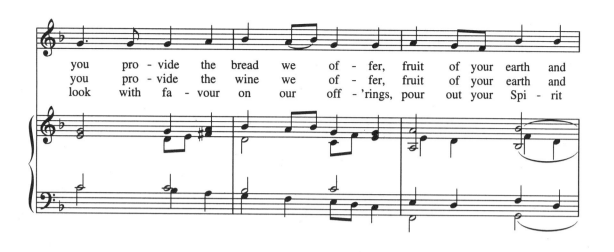

you   pro - vide the bread we of - fer, fruit of your earth and
you   pro - vide the wine we of - fer, fruit of your earth and
look with fa - vour on our off - 'rings, pour out your Spi - rit

work of our hands.
work of our hands.   Blest be the Lord for e - ver, A - men,
o - ver these gifts.

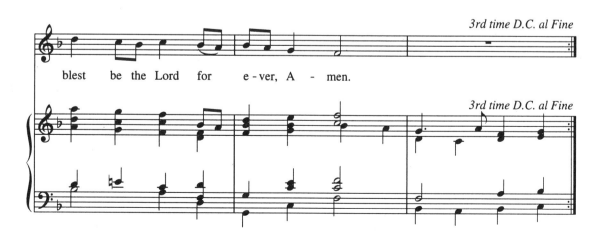

3rd time D.C. al Fine

blest be the Lord for e - ver, A - men.

3rd time D.C. al Fine

LEAD MY PEOPLE TO FREEDOM

Text: Michael Forster
Music: Christopher Tambling

In a jazzy style

1. The voice from the bush said, 'Mo - ses, look snap - py –

have I got a job for you! I've looked a-round and I'm

not ve – ry hap - py: here is what you have to do:

Refrain

Lead my peo - ple to free - dom! Lead my peo - ple to free - dom!

Lead my peo - ple to free - dom! Got to go to the pro - mised land!'

2. The people of God were suff'ring and dying,
   they were sick of slavery.
   All God could hear was the sound of their crying;
   Moses had to set them free.

3. We know that the world is still full of sorrow:
   people need to be set free.
   We've got to give them a better tomorrow,
   so God says to you and me:

SONG FOR A YOUNG PROPHET

Text (based on Jeremiah 1) and Music: Damian Lundy
Arranged by Malcolm Archer

mind.

Last time

rall.

1. Be - fore I formed you in the womb I knew you through and through, I chose you to be mine. Be-fore you left your mo-ther's side I called to you, my child, to be my sign.

D.S.

2. I know that you are very young,
   but I will make you strong;
   I'll fill you with my word;
   and you will travel through the land,
   fulfilling my command
   which you have heard.

3. And ev'rywhere you are to go
   my hand will follow you;
   you will not be alone.
   In all the danger that you fear
   you'll find me very near,
   your word's my own.

4. With all my strength you will be filled;
   you will destroy and build,
   for that is my design.
   You will create and overthrow,
   reap harvests I will sow;
   your word is mine.

ONE HUNDRED AND FIFTY-THREE

Text: Michael Forster
Music: Christopher Tambling

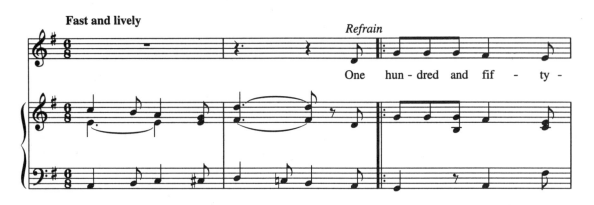

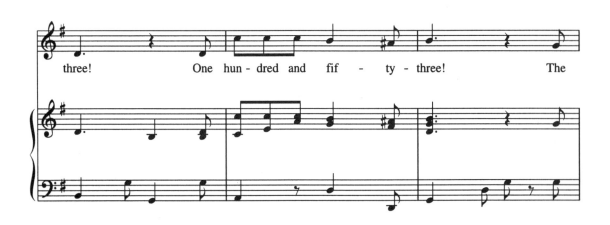

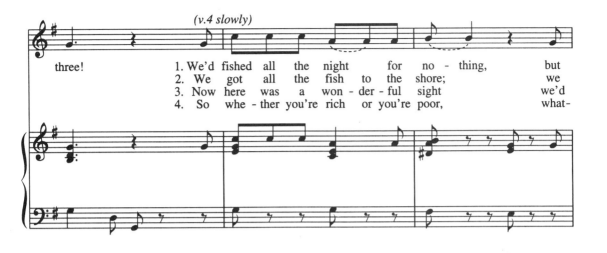

(v.4 slowly)

three!

1. We'd fished all the night for no - thing, but
2. We got all the fish to the shore; we
3. Now here was a won - der - ful sight we'd
4. So whe - ther you're rich or you're poor, what-

Je - sus said, 'Try once more,' So we doubt - ful - ly tried on the
won - dered how ma - ny there'd be. So we start - ed to count, and
ne - ver ex - pec - ted to see. And the net did - n't break; it was
e - ver your race or your sect; be you black, white or brown, Je - sus

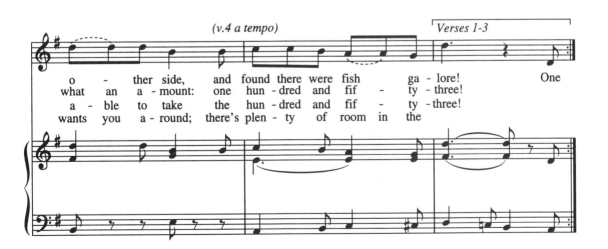

(v.4 a tempo)   *Verses 1-3*

o - ther side, and found there were fish ga - lore! One
what an a - mount: one hun - dred and fif - ty - three!
a - ble to take the hun - dred and fif - ty - three!
wants you a - round; there's plen - ty of room in the

15

Verse 4

net! One hun - dred and fif - ty - three! One

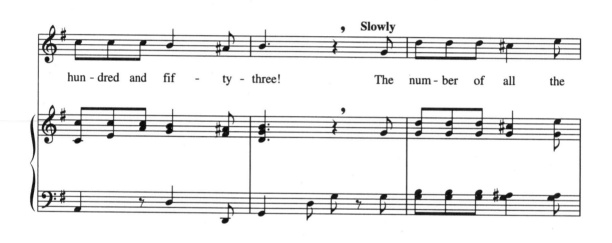

hun - dred and fif – ty - three! *Slowly* The num - ber of all the

Tempo I

fish in the sea: one hun - dred and fif – ty - three!

For the Saint Edmund's Young People's Choir

O ETERNAL GOD

Text: Jeremy Taylor (1613-1667)
Music: Kevin Mayhew

I bless and glo-ri-fy your name; I a-dore your good-ness

and de-light in your love. Take from me ev-'ry

cresc.

ten-den-cy to-ward sin or va-ni-ty; let my de-sires soar

cresc.

up - wards to your love, that I may hun - ger and

thirst for the bread of life and the wine of

heav'n, and know no love but yours.

PRAISE OUR GOD

Text: Hubert J. Richards
Music: Andrew Moore

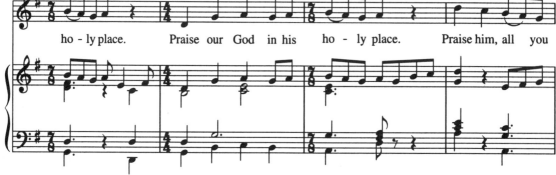

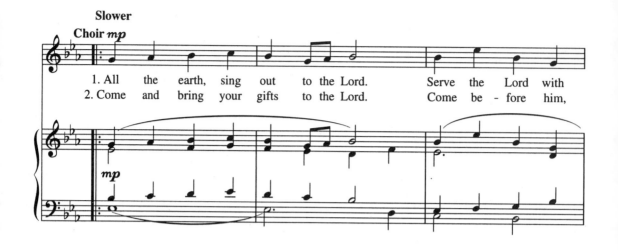

Slower
Choir *mp*

1. All the earth, sing out to the Lord. Serve the Lord with
2. Come and bring your gifts to the Lord. Come be - fore him,

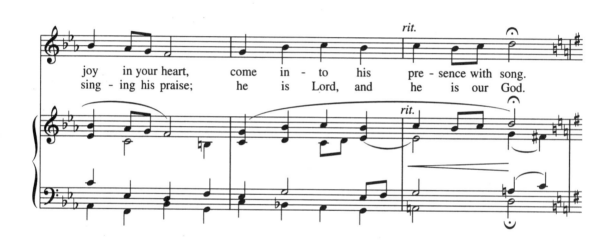

joy in your heart, come in - to his pre - sence with song.
sing - ing his praise; he is Lord, and he is our God.

rit.

Tempo I
Solo *f* **Choir and Congregation**

Al - le - lu - ia, al - le - lu - ia. Al - le - lu - ia, al - le - lu - ia.

Al - le - lu - ia, al - le - lu - ia.

3. God is good, his love ne-ver ends; he is al - ways

true to his word, he is faith - ful, age u-pon age.

LISTEN

Text and Music: Aniceto Nazareth
Arranged by Malcolm Archer

Lis - ten, let your heart keep seek - ing; lis - ten to his con - stant speak - ing;

sempre staccato

lis - ten to the Spi - rit call - ing you.

Lis - ten to his in - spi - ra - tion; lis - ten to his in - vi - ta - tion;

lis - ten   to the Spi - rit   call -ing   you.

1. He's   in the sound of the   thun - der,   in the whis - per   of the breeze.
2. He's   in the laugh - ter of child - ren,   in the pat - ter   of the rain.
3. He's   in the noise of the ci - ty,   in the sing - ing   of the birds.

legato

He's in the might of the whirl - wind,   in the roar - ing   of the seas.
Hear him in cries of the suff - 'ring,   in their moan - ing   and their pain.
And in the night - time, the still - ness   helps you lis - ten   to his word.

D.S.

CODA **Solo soprano**

pp   *rall.*

Lis - ten   to the Spi - rit   call - ing   you.

Ped.

I'M BLACK, I'M WHITE, I'M SHORT, I'M TALL

Text: Michael Forster
Music: Christopher Tambling

1. I'm black, I'm white, I'm short, I'm tall, I'm all the hu-man

race; I'm young, I'm old, I'm large, I'm small, and

Je - sus knows my face. The love of God is

free to ev - 'ry - one, free to ev - 'ry - one, free to ev - 'ry - one.

The love of God is free, oh yes! That's what the gos - pel says.

2. I'm rich, I'm poor, I'm pleased, I'm sad,
   I'm ev'ryone you see.
   I'm quick, I'm slow, I'm good, I'm bad,
   I know that God loves me.

3. So tall and thin, and short and wide,
   and any shade of face,
   I'm one of those for whom Christ died,
   part of the human race!

AVE VERUM CORPUS

Text: 14th Century
Music: Wolfgang Amadeus Mozart (1756-1791)
Arranged by Alan Ridout

Translation: Hail, true body born of the Virgin Mary which truly suffered and was sacrificed on the cross for the human race, whose pierced side poured with water and blood: be to us a foretaste of the verdict to be passed at death.

Cu - jus la - tus per - fo - ra - tum

Cu - jus la - tus per - fo - ra - tum

Man.

un - da flux - it et san - gui - ne;

un - da flux - it et san - gui - ne;

es - to no - bis prae - gu - sta - tum in

es - to no - bis prae - gu - sta - tum in

30

mor - tis ex - a - mi - ne, in

mor - tis ex - a - mi - ne,

mor - tis ex -

in mor - tis ex -

a - mi - ne.

a - mi - ne.

BEHOLD, THE LORD WILL COME!

Text: Michael Forster
Music: Colin Mawby

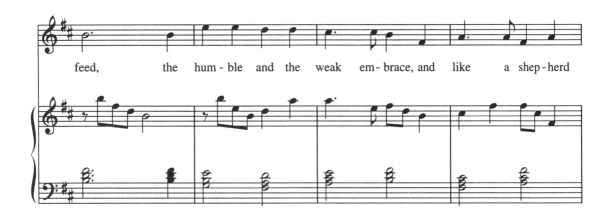

feed, the hum-ble and the weak em-brace, and like a shep-herd

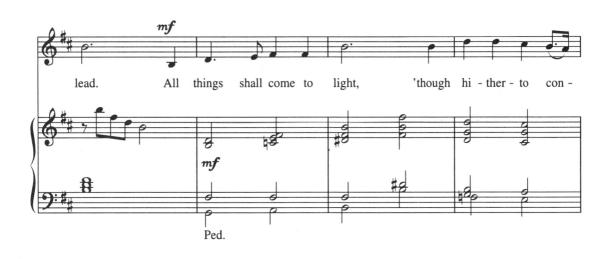

lead. All things shall come to light, 'though hi-ther-to con-

Ped.

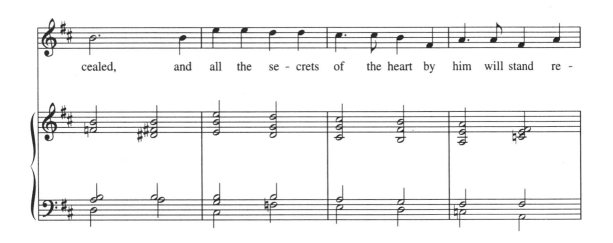

cealed, and all the se-crets of the heart by him will stand re-

ALLELUIA

Text: 1 Samuel 3: 9; John 6: 68
Music: Richard Lloyd

Al - le - lu - ia, al - le - lu - ia, al - le - lu - ia, al - le - lu - ia!

Speak, Lord, your ser-vant is lis-ten-ing: you have the mes-sage of e - ter - nal life.

WHAT KIND OF MAN WAS THIS

Text: Michael Forster
Music: Christopher Tambling

giv - ing words   his per - fect   na - ture prove?   What   kind   of

man   was this,   what   kind   of   love?   4. What   kind   of

Voices or instrument (Optional)

Ah,   ah,

man   was this,   who helped us   all   to   see   the full - ness

GREAT INDEED ARE YOUR WORKS, O LORD

Text and Music: Aniceto Nazareth

1. The u - ni - verse, night and day, tells of all your
2. You are the path which we tread, you will lead us
3. You lead them all by the hand to the heav'n - ly

1. The u - ni - verse, night and day, tells of all your
2. You are the path which we tread, you will lead us
3. You lead them all by the hand to the heav'n - ly

won - ders. You are our life and our light:
on - ward. From ev - 'ry cor - ner of earth
king - dom. Then, at the end of all times,

won - ders. You are our life and our light:
on - ward. From ev - 'ry cor - ner of earth
king - dom. Then, at the end of all times,

D.C.

we shall praise you al - ways.
all the na - tions ga - ther.
you will come in glo - ry.

we shall praise you al - ways.
all the na - tions ga - ther.
you will come in glo - ry.

D.C.

41

I WILL BE WITH YOU

Text (based on Matthew 28:19-20) and Music: Gerard Markland
Arranged by Christopher Tambling

I WILL BLESS THE LORD

Text: Susan Sayers (based on Psalm 33)
Music: Andrew Moore

God. In ev - 'ry - one I meet, in ev - 'ry - thing I see I will sing your praise, O Lord.

2. When I was in pain, when I lived in fear,
    I was calling out to him.
    He rescued me from death, he wiped my tears away,
    I will sing your praise, O Lord.

3. Trust him with your life, trust him with today,
    come and praise the Lord with me;
    O come and know his love, O taste and understand,
    let us sing your praise, O Lord.

BIGGEST ISN'T ALWAYS BEST

Text: Michael Forster
Music: Christopher Tambling

With vigour

1. Go - liath was big and Go - liath was strong; his sword was sharp and his spear was long: he bragged and boas - ted, but he was wrong: big - gest is - n't al - ways best!

2. A shepherd boy had a stone and sling;
   he killed Goliath and amazed the king!
   The people cheered and began to sing,
   'Biggest isn't always best!'

3. So creatures made in a smaller size,
   like tiny sparrows and butterflies,
   are greater than we may realise;
   biggest isn't always best!

LET OUR PRAISE TO YOU

Text: Bryan Spinks (based on Psalm 141)
Music: Malcolm Archer

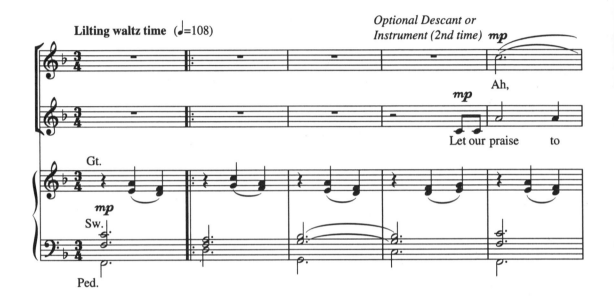

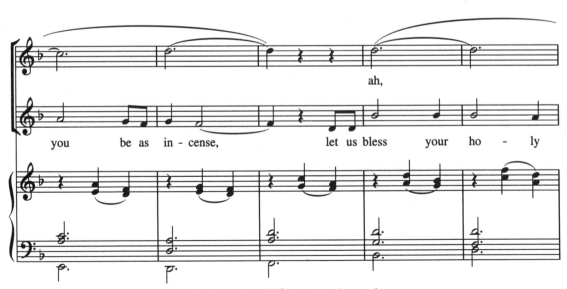

PRAISE TO THE LORD

Text: Hubert J. Richards (based on Psalm 95)
Music: Richard Lloyd

Bles-sed be God for e-ver, A - men, bles-sed be God for e-ver, A - men,

bles-sed be God for e-ver, A - men.

Choir and Congregation

Bles-sed be God for e-ver, A - men,

Ped.

bles-sed be God for e-ver, A - men, bles-sed be God for e-ver, A - men.

Choir *mf*

1. Come, sing a new song to the Lord; come, sing to the Lord,
3. Let all cre-a - tion shout for joy; come, wor-ship the Lord

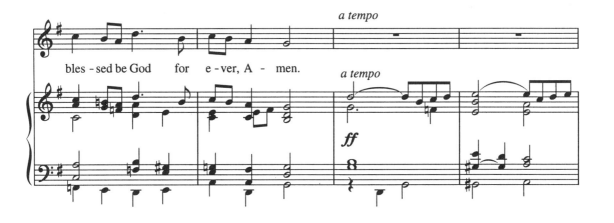

bles - sed be God   for   e - ver, A -   men.

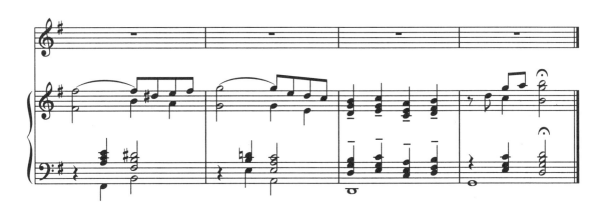

JESUS TURNED THE WATER INTO WINE

Text: Michael Forster
Music: Christopher Tambling

SEND FORTH YOUR SPIRIT, O LORD

Text (based on Psalm 104) and Music: Aniceto Nazareth

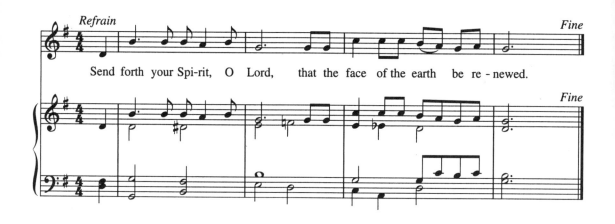

Send forth your Spi-rit, O Lord, that the face of the earth be re - newed.

Ah, ah,

1. O my soul, a - rise and bless the Lord God. Say to

2. 'You have built your palace on the waters.
   Like the winds, the angels do your word.
   You have set the earth on its foundations,
   so firm, to be shaken no more.'

3. 'All your creatures look to you for comfort;
   from your open hand they have their fill.
   You send forth your Spirit and revive them,
   the face of the earth you renew.'

4. While I live, I sing the Lord God's praises;
   I will thank the author of these marvels.
   Praise to God, the Father, Son and Spirit
   both now and for ever. Amen.

THE SHEPHERD WHO CARES

Text: Michael Forster (based on Psalm 22/23)
Music: Christopher Tambling

1. God cares for all cre-a-tion as a shep-herd for the sheep, he is ev-'ry-thing the world can ev-er

e-ven in the dark-ness, there's no need to be a-fraid in the sha-dow and the mys-te-ry of

o-thers may as-sail us, he as-sures us of his love,

know his love and good-ness will be with us all our days, as we go in faith where he has gone be-

'I'm the shep - herd who cares for the

sheep,' he says, 'and my pro - mise you

know I will keep,' he says, 'though the

path may be ro - cky and steep,' he says, 'I will

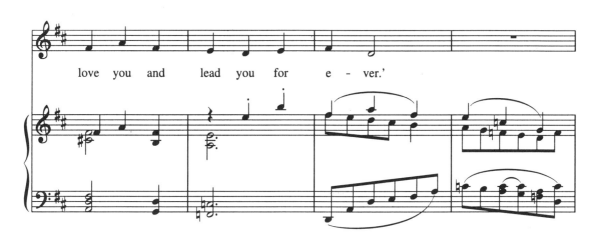

love you and lead you for e - ver.'

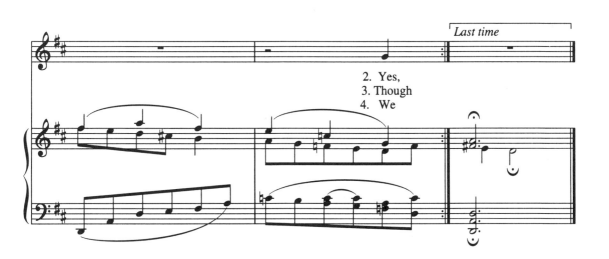

Last time

2. Yes,
3. Though
4. We

TO YOU, O LORD, I LIFT UP MY SOUL

Text: Susan Sayers (based on Psalm 24)
Music: Andrew Moore

Guide my foot - steps in your truth, my Sa - viour and my God.

2. Good and upright is the Lord
who guides the wand'rer back,
leads the humble in this path
and shows the poor his ways.

3. Faithfulness and love abound
for all who keep his word;
those who love him have a friend
whose promise is made clear.

BREAK THE BREAD AND POUR THE WINE

Text: Michael Forster
Music: Christopher Tambling

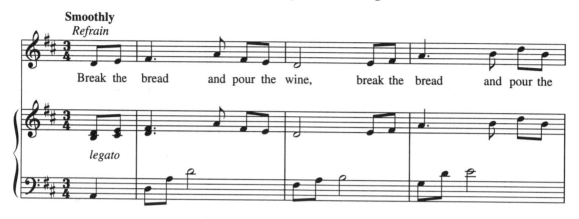

1. Come and meet a-round the ta - ble, God pro-vides the ho-ly food;

D.C.

we can share with one a - no - ther ev - 'ry- thing we have that's good.

D.C.

2. Come and meet around the table,
   God provides the wine to share;
   we enjoy the meal together,
   show each other how we care.

For Judy Long

HOLY GOD

Text: Based on the Aaronic Blessing (Numbers 6:24-26)
Music: Kevin Mayhew

© Copyright 1996 Kevin Mayhew Ltd.
It is illegal to photocopy music.

THE LORD COMES DOWN FROM HEAVEN

Text: Hubert J. Richards (based on Psalm 33)
Music: Andrew Moore

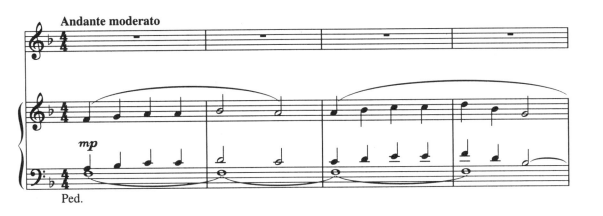

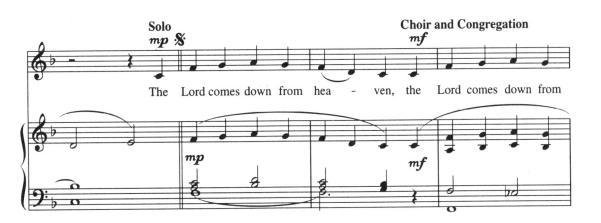

The Lord comes down from hea - ven, the Lord comes down from

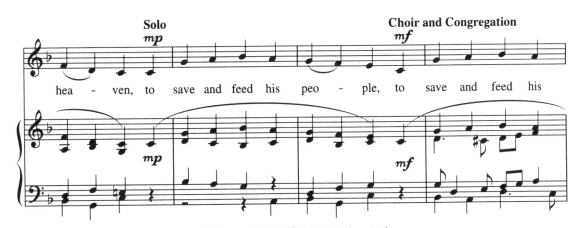

hea - ven, to save and feed his peo - ple, to save and feed his

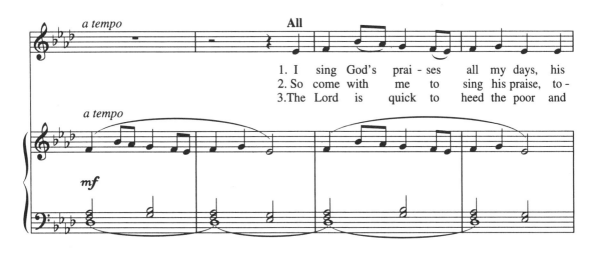

1. I sing God's prai - ses all my days, his
2. So come with me to sing his praise, to -
3. The Lord is quick to heed the poor and

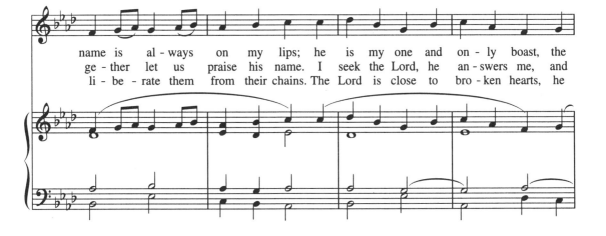

name is al - ways on my lips; he is my one and on - ly boast, the
ge - ther let us praise his name. I seek the Lord, he an - swers me, and
li - be - rate them from their chains. The Lord is close to bro - ken hearts, he

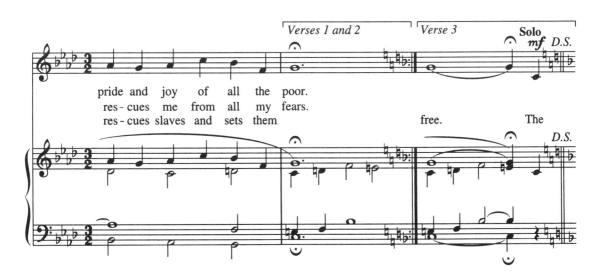

pride and joy of all the poor.
res - cues me from all my fears.
res - cues slaves and sets them free. The

71